THE NICK PAGE SING WITH US SONGBOOK
AUDIENCE SING-ALONGS FOR ALL

FOR USE IN SCHOOLS, CHORUSES AND COMM...
A COMPANION TO THE NICK PAGE
SING WITH US CHORAL SERIES

ONE
Echo to Unison

DEDICATION

I want to dedicate this series of songbooks to the great song leaders who have kept the songs alive in our voices and in our hearts. In particular, I want to thank Dr. Ysaye Maria Barnwell, Pete Seeger, Alice Parker, Jack Langstaff, and Bob Kidd, a wonderful K-5 music teacher in Norman, Oklahoma who leads daily all-school sings.

Nick Page

TABLE OF CONTENTS

HAL•LEONARD® CORPORATION

7777 W. BLUEMOUND RD. P.O. BOX 13819 MILWAUKEE, WI 53213

Visit Hal Leonard Online
at **www.halleonard.com**

The art of the audience sing-along has been rejuvenated in recent years through the work of song leaders like Dr. Ysaye Maria Barnwell and Alice Parker. They have shown that we can all be quite amazing as singers when invited. My book *Sing and Shine On: An Innovative Guide to Leading Multicultural Song* (World Music Press) first expressed my joy of community singing with simple guidelines. The *Sing With Us* songbooks and the accompanying *Sing With Us* choral series – the songs and lyrics as well as the cultural information – are the next step necessary to make the songs come alive.

Alice Parker makes the simple proclamation, "You get what you ask for." When she is inviting audiences of all ages to sing along, she expects wonderful results. She gets what she asks for. If we begin with the assumption that most people are tone deaf and can't sing their way out of a paper bag, then our results will not be very impressive. Yes, there are people of all ages who haven't yet learned how to sing in tune, but they can learn (see appendix) and they can learn to sing well through a series of simple tips. In our minds, we create a hierarchy that divides the talented from the untalented, but let's wipe that divide away. We are all amazing and capable of great community singing.

This book is STEP ONE. It features simple songs to get people started. These are songs for beginners as well as experienced singers of all ages, children and adults. Some songs like "I Walk in Beauty" are intended primarily for younger singers while others are more appropriate for older singers. I like to think of most of the songs as being multi-generational.

I also like to think of all the songs as being multicultural, expressing the joys of many cultures and ultimately creating one voice – the voices of our communities. These songs are kept alive through our singing them; a family gathered around a fire to sing "Cockles and Mussels," an adult choir triumphantly singing "There's Honey in the Rock," or school children singing "Head and Shoulders." Each of these communities is its own culture. The songs help to define who they are. Each community then shapes the songs through their individual voices. The music becomes a living thing – evolving and continually being reborn. Why? Because we sing them.

Throughout the book, I remind readers to honor the cultural roots of each song, to tell the stories and respect the traditions. We sometimes make the incorrect assumption that all music belongs to us and that we can do whatever we want with the songs that we sing. We are allowed to change words within the folk tradition, but the new words must never dishonor the original intent of the song. Rather than owning the songs, we become stewards – guiding the songs along on their journeys. Folk songs from many styles call out for new harmonies, new rhythms and new textures – but the original intent must remain. The song must be kept alive. We keep the music alive by honoring it, respecting it. My website (www.nickmusic.com) has some further essays on singing the music of many cultures including some simple do's and don'ts.

> **"YOU GET WHAT YOU ASK FOR."**
> – ALICE PARKER

This STEP ONE songbook is for all ages. They are the first songs I might lead whether singing with young children or senior citizens, high school choral groups or seasoned adult choirs. The songs can be used wherever a group has gathered. For students, this can mean the classroom, an assembly, or a performance at the school or elsewhere (a senior center, for example). For choral groups of all ages, many of the songs can be performed without audience involvement, but most of these songs were arranged to be added to a concert program as a way to bring in the audience. Anthony Leach, a professor at Penn State and one of the leading authorities on the African-American Spiritual, often has his choirs perform an arrangement of a spiritual followed by an audience sing-along of the same song in a simpler, less arranged manner. Many choral groups will end a concert with the audience standing to sing a rousing patriotic song (see "America, the Beautiful"). My own Mystic Chorale of Boston brings in the audience on one-third of the songs at each concert. Sometimes it will be just the Refrain on a longer song like "A Promise I Will Keep" or "Ale Brider." Sometimes it will be an entire song, like the well-known "Swing Low, Sweet Chariot."

...BROUGHT TOGETHER THROUGH SONG.

One of my heroes, Bob Kidd, teaches music K-5 in Norman, Oklahoma. Every school day begins with an all-school sing. They sing a patriotic song, salute the flag,

Bob Kidd

make announcements, then end with one more song. Sometimes that closing song will feature a class that has prepared some verses with the Refrain sung by the whole school. Sometimes a soloist will sing. I have never seen a more energized school than Bob Kidd's school. The children seem super-attentive, super-charged, and absolutely in love with who they are as learners and as vital parts of a living community. They are brought together through song.

But the songs in this book can also be used in classroom settings or at any community gathering. Teachers at a faculty meeting could begin their meeting by singing "Music Makes Us Whole." The singing will charge their minds – music has that effect. Families and friends at a birthday party could sing "Birthday Swing."

I am a huge believer in schools for all ages having monthly, weekly, or even daily All-School Sings. These can feature between two and eight songs in a variety of styles and levels of simplicity. Often there is an argument that music, certainly a singing assembly, is an unnecessary frill – secondary to academics. But the evidence is showing that music is an aid to all academic skills like listening, attention span, retention, discipline, and emotional well-being. There is an added benefit to the All-School Sings. It lifts the morale of the school. Bob Kidd's students in Norman, Oklahoma love going to school. They are charged by the experience and I believe his daily All-School Sings are the reason why. They simply love being there. They love helping to shape their community – who they are. They own it. This is a powerful statement. Schools should never be learning factories. They must be alive with the creative and emotional expression inherent in all of us.

I will constantly use the phrase "make the songs come alive." It is our creativity and our emotions that bring songs to life. A folk song is not a museum piece, but a living thing. Unless we are singing someone's arrangement, we are allowed to respectfully create new rhythms, melodies, words and even harmonies (see appendix). A song like "This Little Light of Mine" can sound deadly when sung in a stiff manner. We make it come alive when we let it swing and let it pour from our hearts (see "Shine, Shine, Shine"). Music, at its core, is an emotional expression. Long ago, the first mother held her child and sang the first song. It was a love song and it was simply "Ah." The child sang the second song, echoing "Ah." The mother looked at the moon and toned "Oo" and the child echoed "Oo." You can go anywhere on the planet, no matter what language people speak, and the vowel "Oo" will have a universal meaning. Our singing is born of these emotions and these simple expressions. Invite your singers and your audiences to feel what they are singing. Tell them the stories that make the songs come alive. I have provided many of these stories, like the one accompanying the South African song "Thula Klizeo," but further stories can come from your own experience and the experience of your singers.

Most of the songs should be taught in the rote process. Many trained music teachers like myself were taught that the rote process was "dumbing down." Let's change that. Let's make the rote process a process of waking up the ears and the brain – of getting the body and the emotions going! The book begins with simple echo songs for all ages. It is important that the singers listen with great attentiveness, repeating the phrases they are given. I have worked with five year olds, being told not to expect much in the way of attention span. I will ask the children to listen to a simple four beat clapped pattern. Then I will ask them to repeat it. If they don't get it right, I will pause, smile and quietly say, "That's not what I did. Some of you need to listen better." It may take a few tries, but I won't go on until they get it. I have a signal (see "The Zest Song") where I pretend to polish my nails on my shirt lapels. The signal means "good job." When I signal "good job" to the five year olds, they suddenly sit up straight and they become good listeners. The rote process must be one that creates good listening, longer attention spans, lots of movement and lots of emotion – think operatic proportions. Expect great things.

"MAKE THE SONGS COME ALIVE"
– NICK PAGE

In each of the three song sections, the songs for younger children will be provided first with the more challenging songs at the end of each section. Easy songs like "Music Makes Us Whole," can, of course, be sung by all ages, and young children can learn the Refrain to a more challenging song like "There's Honey in the Rock." So most of the songs are actually multi-generational.

The first section of songs are the **ECHO** songs. With the exception of "Shine, Shine, Shine," which has a tricky introduction (that can be omitted), all the echo songs can be taught by rote with everyone repeating after the leader. You can, or course, provide word sheets for some of the songs with children. Reading along is, after all, an academic skill. Songs like "School Song" and "Music Makes Us Whole" have word sheets that can be projected on the wall or be copied. The music, unless otherwise noted, should not be copied.

A **CALL AND RESPONSE** song is a song where the response is different from the call. The responses will have to be taught either by rote or with the lyric sheets. Most of the songs can be sung by all ages. The harmonies provided throughout the book are optional and are intended for older singers.

The final song section features **UNISON** songs. Most accompaniments are suggestions that can be augmented by the player (or replaced with a guitar or other instrument). A cappella singing is a necessary challenge for singers of all ages. Try to honor the requests for a cappella singing. There is great beauty to a simple melody like "There Is More Love Somewhere" when sung without instruments.

Encourage solo singing on verses of songs like "Cockles and Mussels," "Ale Brider" or "There's Honey in the Rock." When individual singers grow in confidence, the whole community grows in confidence.

Your role, with most of these songs, will be that of the song leader. As such, you will be singing most of the songs as a soloist. For concert situations, you can certainly have individuals be the leaders. But if your singers and/or audience are asked to echo, they will be echoing the emotional content along with the words and melodies. If the call is lackluster, then the response will be as well. The leaders must be charged with emotion and energy. Their charge will charge the singers.

When I refer to "your singers," this can mean your classroom, your chorus or your community. When I refer to "your audience," I am referring to a concert situation where your singers have learned the music ahead of time and are now engaging the audience. If you never intend to share these songs with an audience, and that is fine, please ignore those references.

One of your concerts could feature one sing-along or many. Start with a simple echo song followed by a song they already know. Once they are warmed up, teach them a simple unison song.

Many of the world's music traditions have no concept of performances. Most traditions feature celebrations. Think of every sing-along as a celebration – an act of joyous compassion – making the world a more beautiful place by bringing our voices together through song!

LEADER: "Go like this." *(leader blows on right hand fingernails)*
"Go like this." *(leader polishes fingernails on shirt lapel)*
(keep polishing) "Repeat after me: We are the best." (echo)

NOTE: If they don't articulate the "T" on the word "best," then they aren't listening. Say, "Some of you heard a 'T'. Let's see if all of you can hear iT." Never dumb down the rote process. It should require the same discipline that reading music requires.

LEADER: "We are the best!" (echo)
"The very best." (echo)
"We're not snobs." (echo)
"We're simply the best." (echo)
"I'm not better than you." (echo)
"You're not better than me." (echo)
"But we're the best." (echo)
(raising hands zestfully in the air) "WE HAVE ZEST!!!" (echo)

NOTE: Sometimes at this point if one of the singers shows a great deal of zest and expression, you can bring them up as an icebreaker - see appendix. The volunteer's energy will inspire great energy from everyone else.

LEADER: *(lowering hands and leaning over in a "blah" expression)*
"We have no blahs." (echo)
(hands in the air) "ZEST" (echo)
(with blah) "Blah" (echo)

NOTE: This can then become a fun game where they echo and mirror alternating ZESTS and BLAHS with false starts and lots of expression, ending with a fast repeat sequence of "Zest Blah Zest Blah Zest Blah."

LEADER: "We can listen" (echo)
"Listen with ZEST" (echo)

NOTE: Then you are ready to sing these phrases. Be sure that they echo them accurately.

Echo Song

The Zest Song

By NICK PAGE

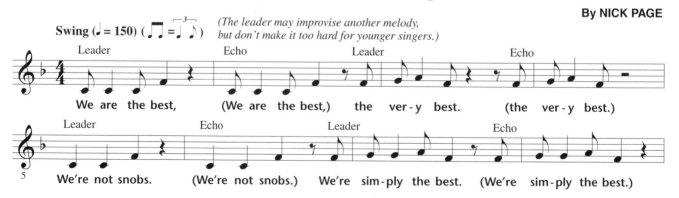

This next section is optional, but fun!

Spoken (or rapped) by leader (or group)

33 If your pos - ture is a - tro - cious, and your bod - y kind of sags, if your
feel - in' kind of blue, ___ want to veg out on T. V., if the

36 brain is lack - in' fo - cus; you got blahs, } You got the
world has got to you, ___ you got blahs,

38 blah, blah, blah, ___ blah, blah, ___ blah, blah, ___ blah, blahs. ___ { But if your
But if you're

(have them mirror your good posture)

41 pos - ture's real - ly awe - some, and your brain is real - ly sharp, and you
feel - in' quite ter - rif - ic, and your brain is real - ly sharp, and your

43 feel you're gon - na blos - som; you got Zest! } You got the
sing - in' is i - dyl - lic; you got Zest!

45 Ze, Ze, Ze, Ze, ___ Ze, ___ Ze, Ze, ___ Ze, Zest! ___ [1] [2] D.C. al Fine
If you're

8

This is an easy echo song with a good message that can be sung with young and old. Get everyone marching in place, then call out each phrase. Encourage harmonies on the echoes. As with all echo songs, insist that they listen well and echo the rhythms, inflections and tones exactly as you sing them. To make it interesting, keep changing the rhythms, melodies, inflections, styles, and tones. For example, on "jazz and funk and rock and roll" play air guitar and make it rock. On "music makes things really neat," you can sing very prim and proper. Use operatic styles, blues, hip hop, etc. In other words, have fun with it! Have the singers take turns being the leaders, then make up new verses about the many benefits of music (and why we dig it).

Music Makes Us Whole

Words by ALDONNA GIROUARD
Used by permission
Arranged by NICK PAGE

3. Music helps us all to feel;
   Keep the beat and keep it real.
   Singing jazz and singing blues,
   Proves to us that music rules!

4. Music is so fun indeed.
   Music makes us all succeed.
   Even when you're feeling blue,
   Music can be true to you.   REFRAIN

5. Jazz and funk and rock and roll;
   Music helps you keep your goal.
   Sing it high or sing it low.
   Music always makes you grow.

6. Dancing, singing, clapping too;
   It can always sound brand new.
   Music makes things really neat.
   You can really feel the beat.   REFRAIN

This song combines echo and call & response formats. Teach the REFRAIN (with the "and celebration" response) ahead of time. Then have the singers echo (and respond) after the leader. When the students know the song better, they can take turns being the leaders. You don't have to sing all the verses, and you can write new verses about math, reading, writing, respect, diversity, history, science, recess, lunch, computer lab, library, homework (be nice), social studies, drama, art, and many other topics. The song was written for all-school sings – events that should happen often. At an all school sing, different classrooms can lead different verses (including new verses).

The singers should raise their hands high every time they sing the word "celebration," holding the fourth "celebration" as long as the leader tells them – you can have fun with this! For even more fun, have them stand then sit every time they sing the word "celebration," staying standing on the fourth (held) "celebration," then sitting immediately after. They will be excited, so you can make "sitting quietly" part of the game plan.

You can add tambourine (on beats 2 & 4) for the REFRAIN. For special occasions, bring in electric bass and other instruments (drum kit, guitar, etc.)

Written for the Loring School in Sudbury, MA

School Song
(What Do You Love About Learning?)

By NICK PAGE

for Leader & Unison Voices
with Piano and optional
percussion and bass

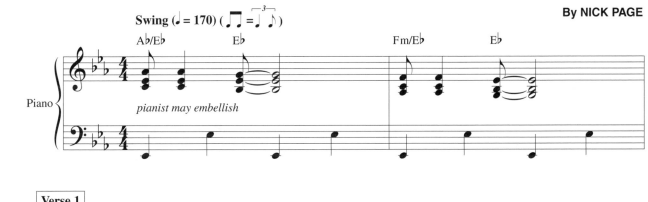

learn - ing?)_ Well, I don't know._ (Well, I don't know.)_

Be - in' a know - it - all,_____ I guess._ (Be - in' a know - it - all,_

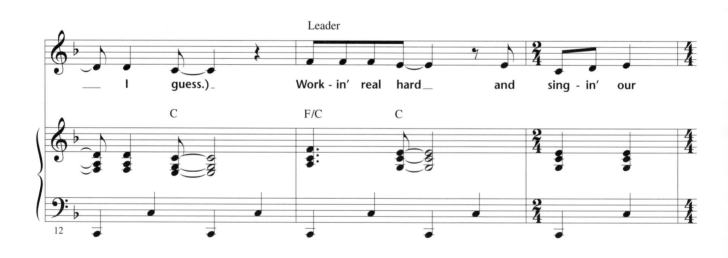

_ I guess.)_ Work - in' real hard_ and sing - in' our

back to Refrain (ms. 15)

* You may ZIP in the name of your school here.

Final Refrain

school song_ a - bout dis - cov - er - y,_ cu - ri-

And cel - e - bra - tion._

os - i - ty,_ cre - a - tiv - i - ty,_

And cel - e - bra - tion._ And cel - e-

bra - tion._ Cel - e - bra - tion._

and com - mun - i - ty._

FROM AUTHOR NICK PAGE: Joseph Shabalala leads the South African's singing group, Ladysmith Black Mambazo. They became world famous when Paul Simon featured them on his Graceland album in the 1980s, but they had already been a national treasure in South Africa. I had the good fortune of spending two weeks with Joseph Shabalala at a workshop he gave at the Omega Retreat Center in Rhinebeck, NY in 1987. He was homesick and had just written a little song called "Thula Klizeo." It means "Be still (Thula) my heart (Klizeo), even here I am at home." It's a joyful song and there's a lot to it!

The leader has to memorize the song to begin with. It should be taught by rote and with lots of energy (emotions). Use dark rich vowels. Begin with teaching the Zulu words in the following sequence: *Thu, thula, klizeo, nalapa, se Ki-ya, Ey-ki-ya. nalapa, se kiya*. Then go back and do the words again with longer phrases: *thula, thula klizeo*, etc. Then you're ready to teach it as an echo song. As with all echo songs, create a discipline that they sing back what you sing them, especially singing back in tune. "Thula Klizeo" is ideal for this because it's opening interval is a minor third, a very accessible interval for beginning singers.

With younger children, use the echo version below, but with older singers (including adults) use the full version featured later in this book. Teach it the same way whether you do the easy echo version or the version where they eventually put it all together. Younger children, even five year olds, will be able to sing the whole song after a few sessions (and they will love it).

Sing percussively and with emotion. Be sure to tell the singers what the words mean and where it's from, then the next time you sing it, tell them again and again. It is essential that singers of all ages know the meaning of the words they sing.

Thula Klizeo
(the echo version)

By JOSEPH SHABALALA
Arranged by NICK PAGE

Dance Steps to "Thula Klizeo"

DANCE
STEPS

The music that Joseph Shabalala composes is from the South African Mbube tradition (from which the song "The Lion Sleeps Tonight" evolved). This music is never sung standing still. I offer two dances, one easy, and one hard (the hard version is later in the book). Both dances are by Joseph Shabalala. Joseph explained that during the Apartheid regime he and his people were banned from doing many of their traditional songs and dances. Many of these dances involved the traditional Zulu stomp, a dance that could shake the earth. As an act of quiet resistance, a new stomp developed. They could dance it and not get in trouble with the authorities. It had secret meaning – a dance of great pride in the Zulu heritage. The new stomp was called Iscatameeya (phonetic spelling). It means to stomp quietly, like a tiptoe – taking great pride in being who you are.

Here are the steps for the easy version of "Thuyla Klizeo." The singers stand in lines and never leave the space they are standing in. It can also be sung by choral groups or by singers in a circle. The right foot is more forward than the left (but not in front of the left foot). The right foot tiptoes down on 1, up on two, down on 3 and up on 4 for the entire song. For the first two phrases (measures 1-4, the arms (at waist level) are extended in front of the belly button, palms facing down. On beats 1 and 3, they honor the earth with a down and up motion like gently needing bread. On the words "Ey Kiya" (beat 3 of measures 3 and 4) the hands reach up high then come down, returning to the needing motion on "nalapa." Joseph explained this reaching gesture as reaching up to bring the powers of God down to earth. It is a gesture common to a lot of South African dance. As with any religious material, public school teachers should be careful to teach what the South Africans believe as opposed to what we should believe. The latter infringes on our Constitutional separation of religion and state while the former honors a culture's religious beliefs without sanitizing it. For schools where religion is a very sensitive issue, you can say "They bring the powers of Heaven down to earth" instead of "the powers of God." It is always best, however, to honor the original intent of the song and everything about a culture, telling its story as completely as possible – to make the tradition come alive.

FROM AUTHOR NICK PAGE: I often teach the dance by having volunteers (a great ice breaker) come up and do a single loud Zulu stomp. I ask everyone to echo: "We are proud." (echo) "We are strong." (echo) "We are Zulu." (echo). Then I have the volunteers do a high kick in the South African style. I say "We are proud." (echo) "We are strong." (echo) "We are Zulu." (echo). Then I have them do a high kick followed by the stomp, repeating the "We are proud" echo phrases. Then I say, "For a long time, Joseph Shabalala and his people were not allowed to do their dances. Is that fair? (They respond "No.") They weren't allowed to sing their traditional songs. Is that fair? (They respond "No.") They weren't allowed to show their pride or their strength. I that fair? (They respond "No.") But then, a new dance emerged called 'is-ca-ta-mee-ya.' (Show the step from above.) It means "to stomp softly, to show your power in a quiet way – with tip-toes." I then have the singers do the step, mirroring me. It is great fun, but it is also not a song or dance to be disrespected through inappropriate behavior from the singers. As a variation, singers can walk in a line while doing the step. It makes a great entrance or exit song.

Notice that with the above description, I never mention racism or hatred. These terms can be very scary for young children. I prefer to phrase it by saying "fair or unfair," which is something they can relate to better. With older singers, you can go into the South African Apartheid period (which ended in 1994) with all of its implications. The song "Thula Klizeo" is from the anti-Apartheid period. Nick Page's book *Sing and Shine On* (www.worldmusicpress.com) devotes an entire chapter to instructing how to teach Thula Klizeo.

This is a beautiful song to invite your audience to sing along on. The lead can be sung by soloists or by small ensembles. The audience simply echoes. If you want to add additional harmony, use the harmonies (in the piano RH), however, the first time through, sing the REFRAIN and Verse 1 with a unison echo to help out the audience. If sung with an audience, it may help to face them while singing the entire song.

When elementary school teacher Donna Nagle sings it with her younger children as a simple echo song, she changes phrases like "my true love and I" to "my true friend and I."

You can vary the tempo in each verse. Let the words dictate the speed. A traditional singer from Wexford County, Ireland named Paddy Berry once told the author, "A song is like a river. Sometimes it wants to flow slowly and sometimes it wants to flow quickly. The words will tell you what to do."

Leader with Echo (echo can be unison or with harmony)

The Water Is Wide

English Folk Song
Arranged by NICK PAGE

(These harmonies may be sung, but sing the echo in unison 1st time.)

The original purchaser of this book has permission to reproduce this song for use in one school only. Any other use is strictly prohibited.

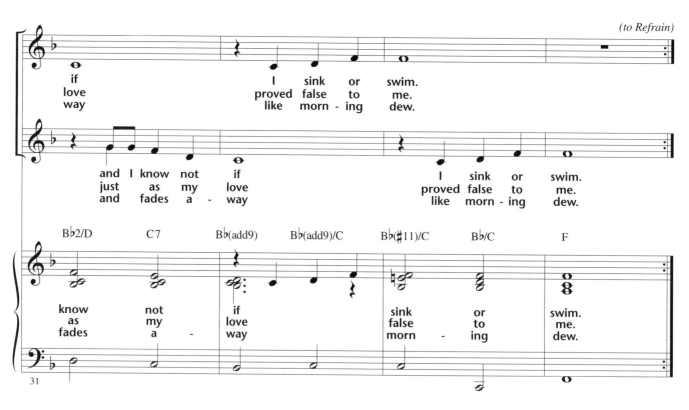

According to Ray Fadden, the Seneca chant Kayowajineh means "I wish you a strong heart." It is pronounced *kah yoh wah jee neh*. When you teach a song like this, find stories from that tradition that help explain the culture. For example, the Seneca people refer to the Seventh Generation saying that everything we do should benefit (and do no harm to) the children born seven generations from now. This is a noble goal, one echoed throughout many of the native traditions. Keep reminding your singers what the words mean, "I wish you a strong heart."

A steady drumbeat on eighth notes can be used throughout. Don't stop the drumbeat as you are talking to your audience. It is important that the drum be a heartbeat. Avoid the cliché of accenting the first of every four beats. This four-beat accent is used only in the old movies which almost always show native people in a negative light. Sing the written accents with great energy. The "hey"s don't have to be sung on pitch. They are joyful shouts.

> **KAYOWAJINEH MEANS "I WISH YOU A STRONG HEART."**
> **– RAY FADDEN**

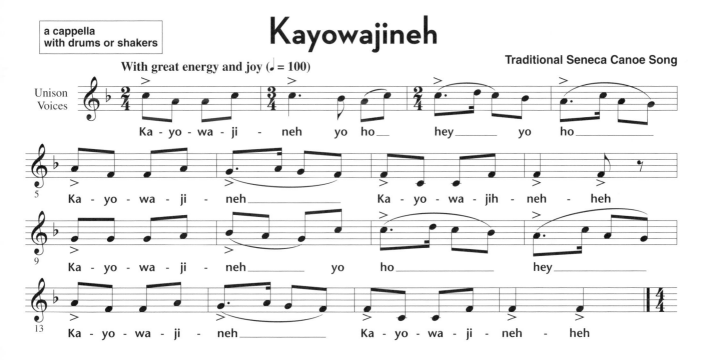

Kayowajineh

a cappella with drums or shakers

Traditional Seneca Canoe Song

With great energy and joy (♩ = 100)

Unison Voices

Ka - yo - wa - ji - neh yo ho hey yo ho

Ka - yo - wa - ji - neh Ka - yo - wa - jih - neh - heh

Ka - yo - wa - ji - neh yo ho hey

Ka - yo - wa - ji - neh Ka - yo - wa - ji - neh - heh

Songs like this should be taught by rote. Passing out the music or the words would be inappropriate. But the song is too difficult to teach to an audience. You can simply have them echo short phrases after you (see next transcription). If possible, have them stand in a circle, facing the inside (with the drum in the middle). Keeping the circle intact, they would step to the right for a verse, then to the left for another verse. If you repeat these echoes enough times, you will be able to return to the original version without the echo.

Most Native Americans have a cherished sense of sacred space and sacred time. We have to be careful to honor this. There are many Native American songs that would be inappropriate for us to sing simply because the place and time we would sing the song are not sacred. The song "Kayowajineh" can be shared. You can respect the song and its tradition by giving it due solemnity, great energy and a living heartbeat. For more info, see Bryan Burton's songbook <u>Moving Within the Circle: Contemporary Native American Music and Dance</u> available from World Music Press.

You can start at a medium tempo and gradually get faster. When you go back to the beginning, you can start it again at a higher pitch. Keep going up in pitch. It can become quite powerful.

This is a rousing West African song of welcoming as sung by the great Baba Olatunji, the Nigerian drummer who popularized West African drumming in North America.

Teach the responses before beginning. Singers will learn them quickly. Tell them what the words mean (always explain what words mean). Baba would lead this with great energy and a booming voice that could be heard above hundreds of drums. If used with drums (and it should be used with drums) the leader will need a microphone. Sing it through slowly first, then bring in the up tempo drums. Then sing the whole song again with the driving pulse. Dancing could ensue (always a good thing with West African drumming). Then sing the song again. You can end by singing measures 9-24 slowly without drums.

Pronunciation: *Fahn-gah (not fang-ga) ah-lah-fee-yah ah-shay ah-shay*

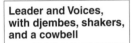

Fanga
Yuroba, West African

Traditional West African Song

shey,　　　　A - shey,＿　A - shey.

A - shey,＿　A - shey,

ff C

A - shey,＿　A - shey.

ff

A - shey,＿　A - shey.　　　　　　A - shey,＿　A - shey.

Begin with many drums playing the low djembe part. Then add the cowbell and shaker. Lastly, add one player on the high djembe part. The spoken part under the shaker rhythm (for rehearsal only) will help the players learn their rhythms.

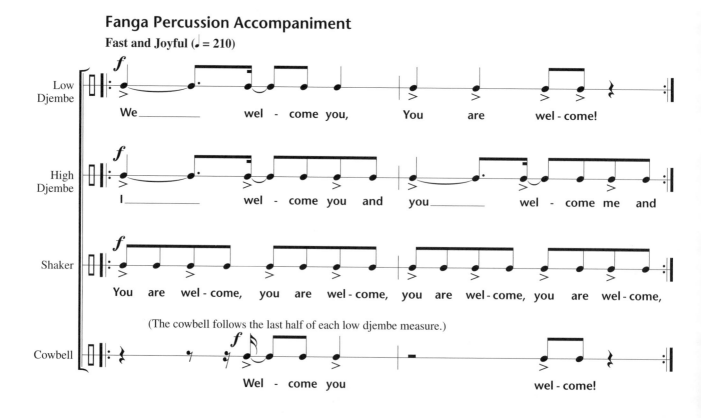

Fanga Percussion Accompaniment

Fast and Joyful (♩ = 210)

Low Djembe *f*

We＿＿＿＿　wel - come you,　　You　are　wel - come!

High Djembe *f*

I＿＿＿＿　wel - come you and　you＿＿＿＿　wel - come me and

Shaker *f*

You　are　wel - come,　you　are　wel - come,　you　are　wel - come,　you　are　wel - come,

(The cowbell follows the last half of each low djembe measure.)

Cowbell *f*

Wel - come you　　　　　　　wel - come!

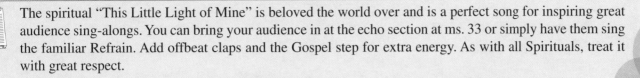

The spiritual "This Little Light of Mine" is beloved the world over and is a perfect song for inspiring great audience sing-alongs. You can bring your audience in at the echo section at ms. 33 or simply have them sing the familiar Refrain. Add offbeat claps and the Gospel step for extra energy. As with all Spirituals, treat it with great respect.

Option: You can sing the arrangement as written or (if the beginning is too hard for your singers) you can begin at the pick-up to ms. 22, and then disregard the repeat in ms. 40 and go on to ms. 41 ("This little light of mine"). At. ms. 55 you can go back to the pickup to ms. 22 again for the second verse that leads in "Everywhere I go" (ms. 41). When you get to ms. 55 the 2nd time, do the normal repeat back to ms. 41 for "All around the world" – ending at ms. 55.

"Shine, Shine, Shine" is also available in an SATB (optional Unison/2-Part) arrangement (Hal Leonard #08745508), Audio Trax (Hal Leonard #08745513).

For the Mystic Chorale

Shine, Shine, Shine

Arranged by NICK PAGE
Based on traditional spiritual
"This Little Light of Mine"

To help cue the audience:
1st time – shout out "Everywhere I go"
2nd time – "All around the world"

(3rd time) **D.C. al Fine**

REFRAIN

Well, this little light, this little light,
　this little light of mine,
I'm gonna let it, I'm gonna let it,
　I'm gonna let it shine.
This little light, this little light,
　this little light of mine,
Let it shine, shine, shine.
Let it shine, shine, shine.
Let it shine, shine, shine all around the world.

1. You can let your light shine
　　out to every child.
　You can let your light shine
　　to the mighty and mild.
　You can let your light shine way deep inside.
　You can shine, shine, shine,
　You can let your light shine. Don't let it hide.

Because you shine for me,
And I shine for you,
And we all shine together.
Oh yes, it's true!

REFRAIN

2. You can let your light shine
　　right where you are.
　You can let your light shine right in your car.
　You can let your light shine down by the sea.
　You can shine, shine, shine,
　You can let your light shine for you and me.

So let's all sing together,
This song we know.
This little Light, ready, set, go!

This little light of mine, I'm gonna let it shine.
This little light of mine, I'm-a gonna let it shine.
This little light of mine, I'm gonna let it shine.
Let it shine, let it shine, let it shine.

Everywhere I go, I'm gonna let it shine.
Everywhere I go, I'm-a gonna let it shine.
Everywhere I go, I'm gonna let it shine.
Let it shine, let it shine, let it shine.

All around the world, I'm gonna let it shine.
All around the world, I'm-a gonna let it shine.
All around the world, I'm gonna let it shine.
Let it shine, let it shine, let it shine.

REFRAIN (*or end here*)

The sea chanties were work songs – songs to relieve the tedium of long hours of labor aboard the old sailing ships.

Have your singers pretend to pull a rope, hands alternately reaching for the next length of rope. On the word "boots," everyone makes a huge, fast tug. Have your singers make up new words, taking turns singing solos, i.e. "We'll finish in time for lunch." Whenever you add words to a song, be respectful of the song's tradition.

Call and Response

To Me Way Hey, To Me Way Oh!

Sea Chantey

* fill in a word suitable for the environment you are in while singing this song

FROM THE AUTHOR: I learned the song at boy scout camp with three hundred boys screaming their hearts out on the joyous "Oh," which the scout master would hold for an impossibly long time, much to our delight! It is the first song I ever led.

 This is an add-on song, beginning with the head and working on down the body. Here are the French words with English translations.

> le tête (the head)
> le nez (the nose)
> le menton (the chin)
> les yeux (the eyes)
> le visage (the face)
> le cou (the neck)
> les pieds (the feet)

Pronounciations:

Ahlooehte, jhahn (soft "j") *teel Ahlooehte,*
Jhuh (soft "j") *te plu* (French "oo" with puckered lips) *mehreh.*

la tête = *lah teht*
le nez = *lu* (French "oo") *ney*
le menton = *lu mehntahw* (accent on "tahw")
les yeux = *lay jhu* (soft "j")
le visage = *lu veezahjhe* (accent on "zah")
le cou = *loo coo*
les pieds = *lay pee-eh* (accent on "eh")

The song teaches itself. The leader sings the Refrain each time with everyone picking it up as you go along. Use hand gestures pointing to your head for "la tête," your feet for "les pieds" or whatever you are singing about. Have fun with it! For example on "le nez," squeeze your nose and make an exaggerated nasal sound. It is an additive song with each verse getting longer and the repetitions of anatomy getting faster. You may add more body parts if you wish. The "Oh" also gets longer and longer. The song works best *a cappella*, sung with great spirit. Find someone who speaks French to help with the pronunciation.

Cecil Sharpe was the great collector and arranger of folk songs from his native England, but also from Scotland, Wales, Ireland and North America. His piano accompaniments are to be enjoyed.

For sing-along purposes, you can divide your audience into the CALL (Jackie Boy) and the RESPONSE (Master) or have them simply do the response. Teach them their parts through simple rote repetition (with a smile). "The Keeper" is, of course, a folk song, which means if you want to write new verses, you are free to do so just as long as you respect the tradition.

This is a great song for teaching children good choral vowels, particularly in the refrain.

Call and Response

The Keeper

English Folk Song
Edited by CECIL SHARPE

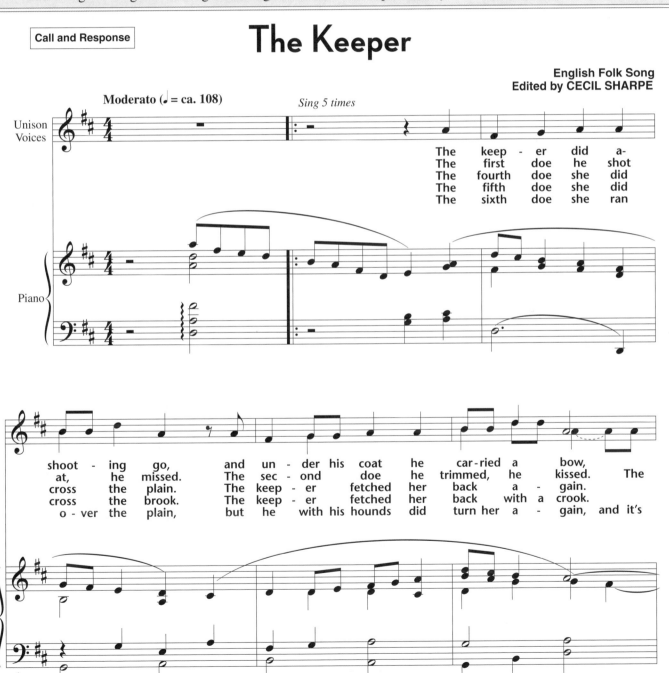

all   for to shoot   at   a   mer - ry lit - tle doe
third doe   went where   no - bod - y   wist
Where she is now she   may   re - main
Where she is now you must go   and   look
there he did hunt   in   a   mer - ry mer - ry vein

a - mong the leaves so____

green - o.   Jack - ie boy!   Sing ye well!

Call

Response

green - o.   Mas - ter!   Ver - y well!

Hey down,   der - ry der - ry down,   a - mong the leaves so____

Ho down,   a - mong the leaves so____

LYRIC SHEET: The Keeper

English Folk Song
Edited by Cecil Sharpe

The keeper did a-shooting go,
And under his coat he carried a bow,
All for to shoot at a merry little doe
    Among the leaves so green-o.

CALL/RESPONSE
Jackie boy! Master! Sing ye well! Very well!
Hey down, Ho down, derry derry down,
    Among the leaves so green-o.
To my hey down down, to my ho down down,
Hey down, ho down, derry derry down,
    Among the leaves so green-o.

The first doe he shot at, he missed.
The second doe he trimmed, he kissed.
The third doe went where nobody wist
    Among the leaves so green-o.

CALL/RESPONSE

The fourth doe she did cross the plain.
The keeper fetched her back again.
Where she is now she may remain
    Among the leaves so green-o.

CALL/RESPONSE

The fifth doe she did cross the brook.
The keeper fetched her back with a crook.
Where she is now you must go and look
    Among the leaves so green-o.

CALL/RESPONSE

The sixth doe she ran over the plain,
But he with his hounds did turn her again,
And it's there he did hunt in a merry merry vein
    Among the leaves so green-o.

CALL/RESPONSE

Imagine your singers and/or audience line dancing with joy through an auditorium or gymnasium. Imagine a rousing spiral dance (see appendix). "Ale Brider" is a joyous Yiddish folksong from Eastern Europe. The Yiddish language comes from an older German dialect, but the spirit of this song comes from the deep wellspring of Jewish tradition.

If you choose to involve your audience, have your singers sing the Refrain once through. Then invite the audience to sing along with you on the Refrain. During the opening VAMP, you can talk to your audience and get them in the mood. Have them shout the words "Oy Oy Oy" with great emotion. If they don't emote, invite them to let it all out – JOY, SORROW – all their emotions! The guide to making a tradition like this come alive is to give it great emotion (without mocking it).

You can write new verses using the same pattern of repetition. For example, "We are happy, We are happy" with the echo "Oy Oy We are happy." Or have someone translate the verses into Spanish, French or other languages. After the last verse, repeat the Refrain several times, gradually getting faster each time. If possible add a line dance (with the grapevine step).

Pronunciation (similar to German):

1. *Oon mee-ehr tziy-nehn ah-luh bree-deh*
   Oon mee-ehr tzeeng-ehn frray-lehk lee-duh
   Oon mee-ehr hahl-tehn zeek een ay-nehm
   Ah-zehlk-ehs eez nee toh bay kay-nehm

2. *Oon mee-ehr tziy-nehn ah-luh shvehs-teh*
   Vee Soh-ray Reev-kah Root oon Ehsh-teh
   Oon mee-ehr tzay-nehn ah-luh ay-nihk
   Tzee mee-ehr tzay-nehn feel tzee vay-nihk

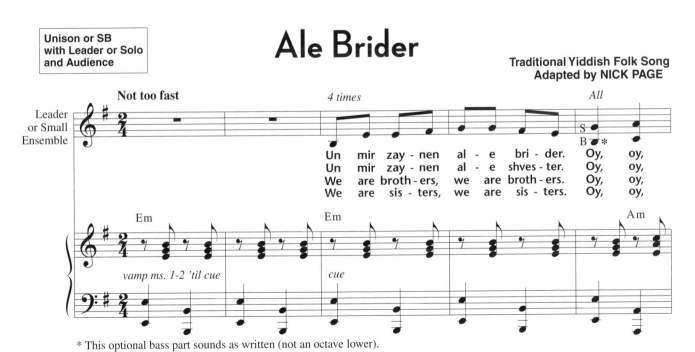

Ale Brider

Traditional Yiddish Folk Song
Adapted by NICK PAGE

Unison or SB
with Leader or Solo
and Audience

Leader or Small Ensemble

Not too fast

4 times

All

Un	mir	zay - nen	al - e	bri - der.	Oy,	oy,
Un	mir	zay - nen	al - e	shves - ter.	Oy,	oy,
We	are	broth - ers,	we are	broth - ers.	Oy,	oy,
We	are	sis - ters,	we are	sis - ters.	Oy,	oy,

Em   Em   Am

vamp ms. 1-2 'til cue   *cue*

* This optional bass part sounds as written (not an octave lower).

* When you have sung all four verses, repeat back to Refrain several times,
getting faster and faster (with a line dance if possible).

1. Un mir zaynen ale brider. Oy, oy, ale brider.
   Un mir zingen freylekhe lider. Oy, oy, oy.
   Un mir haltn zikh in eynem. Oy, oy, zikh in eynem.
   Azelkhes iz ni to bay keynem. Oy, oy, oy.

REFRAIN   Dy dy dy dy dy . . .

2. Un mir zaynen ale shvester. Oy, oy, ale shvester.
   Vi Sore, Rivka, Rut un Ester. Oy, oy, oy.
   Un mir zaynen ale eynik. Oy, oy ale eynik.
   Tzi mir zaynen fil tzi veynik. Oy, oy, oy.

REFRAIN

3. We are brothers, we are brothers. Oy, oy, we are brothers.
   Singin' songs of joy together. Oy, oy, oy.
   Come together, sing together. Oy, oy, sing together.
   What a thrill to be together. Oy, oy, oy.

REFRAIN

4. We are sisters, we are sisters. Oy, oy, we are sisters.
   Rebecca, Sara, Ruth and Esther. Oy, oy, oy.
   All of us are all united. Oy, oy, all united.
   We are family united. Oy, oy, oy.

REFRAIN

AUTHOR NICK PAGE has fond memories of his grandfather singing this song when he was a child. His "Gramp" learned it when he was a pilot stationed in France during World War I. It was an old English dancehall song. The dancehall music was the popular music of the day before the age of radios, records or TV. If you sing this song with your audience, teach the response part and the Refrain first, then sing the whole song with great gusto. You could also sing the whole song twice, getting faster and faster as you go along. You can play with this, doing some verses extremely slow and/or soft and other verses fast and/or boisterous. "Compagnie" is pronounced "com-pah-nee." The "g" is silent. "Vive L'amour" is sung "Veev-eh luh-more."

Vive L'amour

Unison Call and Response
with optional harmony and Piano

Traditional
Adapted by NICK PAGE

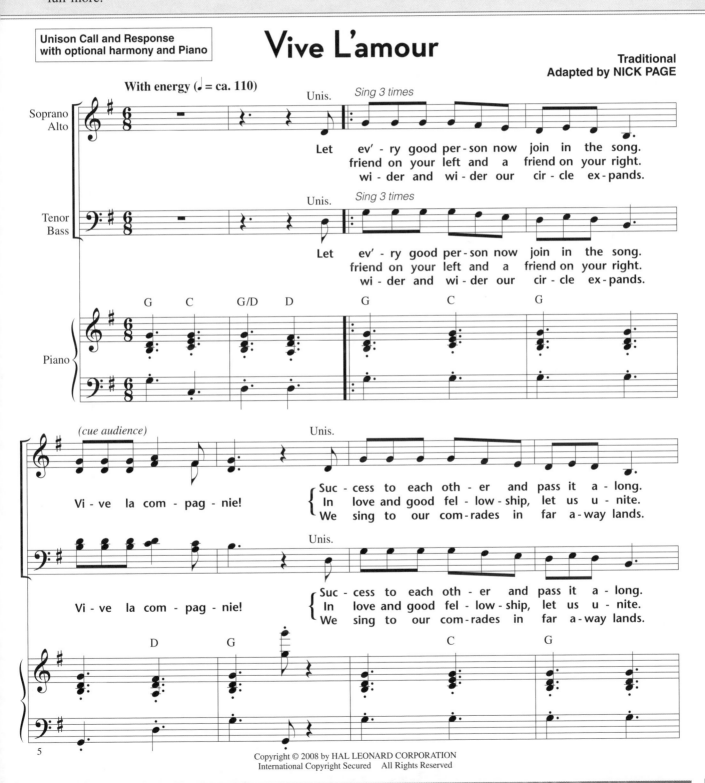

Vive L'amour

SINGER SONGSHEET

Traditional
Adapted by NICK PAGE

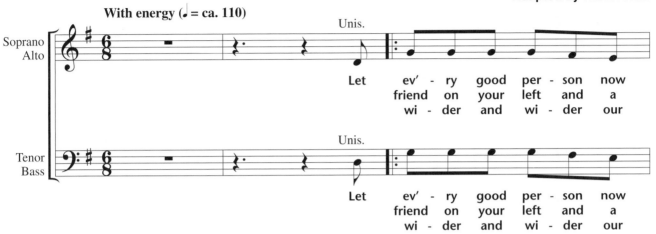

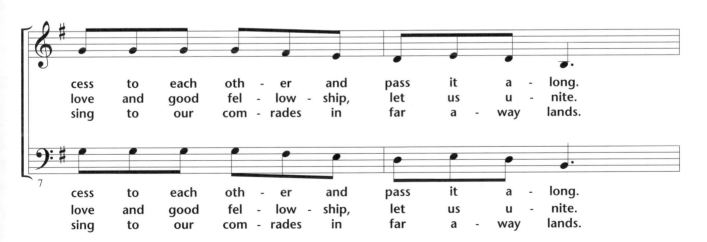

Refrain *(with audience)*

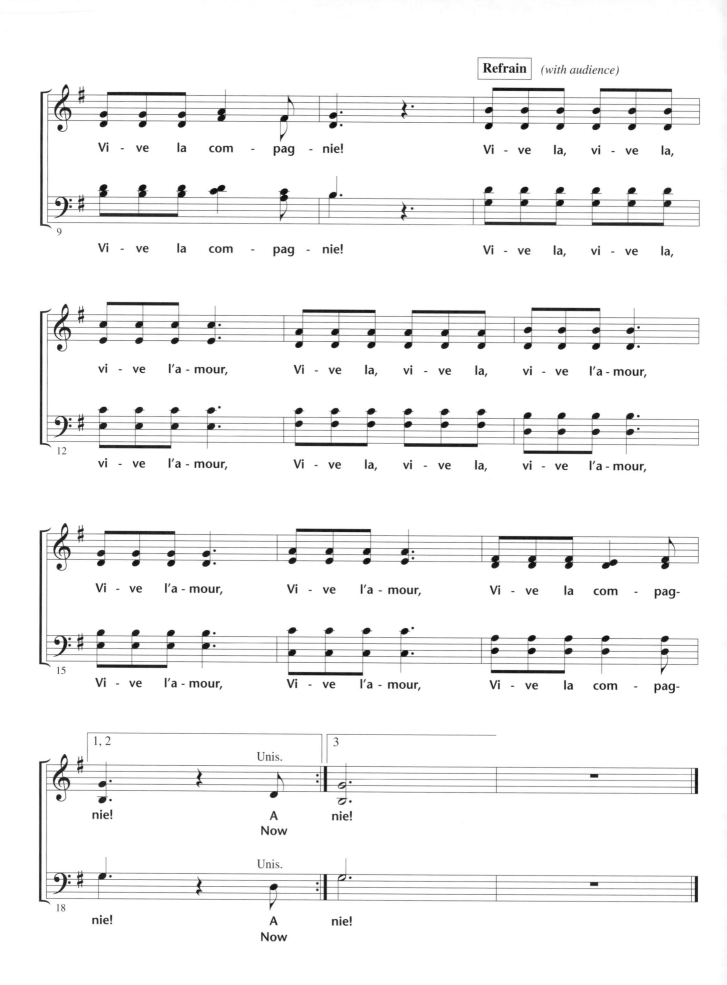

Combining stories with songs is an age-old way to get people singing along. Pete Seeger's "Abiyoyo" is a well known example. The following story explains the meaning of the Navaho concept of walking in beauty. For more information on this, see Bryon Burton's "Moving Within the Circle: Contemporary Native American Music and Dance" available from World Music Press.

This story and song is perfect for younger singers. The piano is optional, as is the descant at the end. The narration can be spoken by the leader, a narrator, or a child (who has been taught to speak slowly and clearly). Ideally, the narration should be memorized ahead of time – or even better, told in the leader's own words).

The leader introduces the song, singing it through once.

Story with Song

I Walk in Beauty

from the Navaho Prayer
Music by NICK PAGE
Story adapted by NICK PAGE
and NITA PENFOLD

LEADER: This is the story of the Coyote who walked in beauty. To tell it, I need a volunteer to be the Coyote. *(A volunteer is chosen and comes up. The leader is holding two egg shakers.)* In many Native American stories, the Coyote is the wisest of all the animals, some-times called the TRICKSTER. *(Leader may expand on this.)* In my hands, I am holding some magic seeds, or at least, we're going to pretend they are magic seeds. Whoever holds these seeds is the CENTER OF THE UNIVERSE, THE MOST IMPORTANT CREATURE IN THE WORLD. Whoever holds these seeds walks in the circle. Who-ever holds these seeds, WALKS IN BEAUTY. *(Leader asks Coyote)* "Are you ready for this awesome responsibility?"

COYOTE: Yes.

LEADER: *(hands one of the eggs to Coyote)* You are now the center of the circle. I want you to walk around this room, to walk in the circle, to walk in beauty. *(Leader sings the song – playing shaker on the quarter note beats as coyote walks to the beat.)*

I walk in beau-ty, Beau-ty be-fore me, Beau-ty be-hind me, Beau-ty a-bove me,
Beau-ty be-low me, Beau-ty with-in me.

LEADER: STOP! It is time to share these magic seeds with the eagle. We need a volunteer to be the eagle. *(A volunteer is chosen who now stands in front of the Coyote, who will follow.)*

LEADER: *(to the eagle)* You are now the center of the circle. Whoever holds these seeds is the CENTER OF THE UNIVERSE, THE MOST IMPORTANT CREATURE IN THE WORLD. Whoever holds these seeds, walks in beauty. Eagle and Coyote please walk in the circle. *(Leader encourages eagle to lift up its' wings.)*

THE SONG IS SUNG AGAIN.

LEADER: STOP! We need a bear. *(A bear is chosen. Be sure to get a mix of both girls and boys.)* You are now the center of the circle. Whoever holds these seeds is the CENTER OF THE UNIVERSE, THE MOST IMPORTANT CREATURE IN THE WORLD. Whoever holds these seeds walks in beauty. Bear, Eagle and Coyote please walk in the circle. *(Leader encourages bear to walk like a bear.)*

THE SONG IS SUNG AGAIN.

Then you can use the same narration, adding more creatures like a snake, a butterfly, and/or a turtle.

LEADER: STOP! We need one of the adults *(or teachers)* in the room. *(An adult is chosen – to the great delight from the children.) (Leader says to adult)* **You are the human being. You are now the center of the circle. Whoever holds these seeds is the CENTER OF THE UNIVERSE, THE MOST IMPORTANT CREATURE IN THE WORLD. Whoever holds these seeds, walks in beauty. Please walk in the circle.** *(Human walks around the room with the volunteer animals following behind.)*

I walk in beau-ty, Beau-ty be-fore me, Beau-ty be-hind me, Beau-ty a-bove me, Beau-ty be-low me, Beau-ty with-in me.

LEADER: *(signals the human to come up front)* **It is now time for you, the human, to share, but the human says, I don't want to share.** *(Human echoes)* **I like being the center.** *(Human echoes)* **No one but me.** *(Human echoes)*

LEADER: **Just then the animals** *(they may be named one by one)* **say to the human, "Hello, Human."** *(Children echo)* **What do YOU want?** *(Human echoes)* **You must learn to share.** *(Children echo)* **I don't want to.** *(Human echoes)*

LEADER: *(to all the children)* **Then all the creatures say, "But you walk in beauty."** *(All children echo)* **What does that mean?** *(Human echoes)* **To walk in beauty** *(Children echo)* **is to walk in the circle.** *(Children echo)* **Coyote is in the circle.** *(Coyote echoes)* **Eagle is in the circle.** *(Eagle echoes)* **Bear is in the circle.** *(Bear echoes)* **Ssssssssnake is in the circle.** *(Snake echoes)* **Human is in the circle.** *(Human echoes)* **All life is in the circle.** *(All echo)* **All life walks in beauty.** *(All echo)* **Which is why** *(All echo)* **WE MUST SHARE.** *(All echo)* **So the human says, "Okay,"** *(Human echoes)* **I'll share.** *(Human echoes)*

LEADER: *(to the volunteers up front)* **Hold out your hands. Human, share your seeds with each of the animals.** *(Human spills pretend seeds into their hands.)* **Now animals, face the audience and when I give the signal, I want you to throw these seeds in the air so EVERYONE CAN BECOME THE CENTER OF THE UNIVERSE – SO EVERYONE CAN WALK IN BEAUTY. Are you ready? Get set, SHARE.** *(They throw the seeds in the air and the children jump up to catch them. When the great joy subsides, sing the song a few more times, perhaps adding the descant (see next page) which they would have had to learn ahead of time. With smaller groups, they can do a simple circle dance walking clockwise, then counter-clockwise.)*

LEADER: And that is what the Navahos mean when they walk in beauty.

With smaller groups, this can be followed by a discussion.
• Who is in the circle?
• Who walks in beauty?
• Can we walk in beauty?

This is one of many songs inspired by the Navaho philosophy "to walk in beauty." For more information, see the song "I Walk in Beauty", page 57, which tells the meaning and source of the Navaho Prayer.

The following hand gestures accompany this song:

"before us"	extended palms facing out
"behind us"	extended palms behind
"under our feet"	palms pushing down to the floor
"within us"	palms crossed covering heart
"let all around us be peace"	one hand makes a circle from waist to above head and back

At the end of each verse, the leader calls out the next verse saying "Joy before us" (love … beauty… or make up your own).

Option 1. Singers can be walking in a circle with one step every three beats.

Option 2. On the phrase "Let all around us be peace," singers may rotate with their arms extended outward in a flowing motion, similar to treading water slowly.

Option 3. Create a medley of chants inspired by the "I Walk in Beauty" chants.

Unison

Peace Before Us

from the Navaho Prayer

Medium (♩ = 120)

1. Peace be - fore us, peace be - hind__ us, peace un - der our
2. Joy…
3. Love…
4. Beauty…

feet. Peace with - in us, peace a - bove__ us, let all a-

round us be peace. Oh,_____ let all a - round us be peace.

This beautiful African-American hymn sounds best when sung *a cappella* with singers adding their own harmonies or simply singing it in unison. You may sing it in a different key and you may add verses – verses that honor the African-American hymn tradition. Keep it humble.

Teach it by rote, phrase by phrase. As with all rote teaching, it is best to go slow, repeating as necessary. Don't ask, "Do you have it yet?" If they can sing it without you singing along, then they know it. This song makes a wonderful song for a closing circle. Teach it earlier in the sing, then as a courtesy, remind them how it goes.

Unison

There Is More Love Somewhere

African-American Hymn

During the Civil Rights movement, African-American hymns like "Somebody Prayed for Me" became "Somebody Marched for Me." These songs of great compassion gave thanks to those who stood for justice, and should be treated with the greatest of respect. You may add harmonies, slow it down, speed it up, add offbeat claps and the Gospel step, and add new words - always being respectful of the tradition. An audience can pick it up after a few repetitions. At the end of each verse, someone simply shouts out the next words.

AUTHOR'S NOTE: I was singing this song with children at a one-year memorial for the victims of 9/11. I asked for a new word to zip in and a child suggested, "Somebody cried for me." It was a powerful moment and proof that music comes alive when we respect it and when we give it our own voice.

Unison

Somebody Prayed for Me

African-American Hymn
Arranged by NICK PAGE

You're never too old to do patty cake. It's a great icebreaker and can create comic relief at the right time. Sing the first three phrases and have everyone repeat them after you. Then sing the last phrase and have them repeat it. If necessary, sing the whole song again before teaching the hand motions.

Motions:

"head"	both hands touch head
"shoulders"	both hands touch shoulders
"baby"	clap own hands
"one"	clap partner's hands
(rest)	clap own hands
"two"	clap partner's hands
(rest)	clap own hands
"three"	clap partner's hands

For "drive the car," turn the steering wheel. All the other movements are self-explanatory. At the end of each verse, shout out the words to the next verse.

Unison

Head and Shoulders, Baby

Children's Action Song

Other Verses: **Honk the horn** *(make honking gesture)*
Hitch a ride *(thumb a ride gesture)*
Milk the cow *(milk a cow)*

Have the singers make up more verses. End with "head and shoulders" again, but really fast.

This old patty cake song can be turned into a simple and joyful new age chant. You will need a space where people can move around. Sing the original version (adults love it), then later in the sing, when everyone is in a closing circle formation, sing the first phrase of the new age version by yourself, placing your hands on your head, then (very slowly) on your heart. Turn to someone who becomes your partner and play the patty cake part very slowly, pressing your palms against your partners palms on "one," "two" and "three." In between each number, bring your palms together as in a prayer. Then bring everyone in on the second phrase as you walk over to someone else to be a new partner. Go very slowly – the slower, the better. Have them model your movements, finding new partners as they go along. End in silence.

Unison

Head and Heart
(The New Age Version)

Adapted by NICK PAGE
(Based on the tune:
"Head and Shoulders")

Very, very slow

Head and heart, ba - by one, two, three. Head and

heart,__ ba - by one, two, three. Head and

heart, ba - by one, two, three. Head and heart,__ head and

heart,__ head and heart,__ ba - by one, two, three.

The words of Katherine Lee Bates (1859-1929) resonate one hundred years after they were written. They speak for people of all political persuasions, whether liberal or conservative. The song makes a fitting close for concerts. Most people will know the first verse, so your singers can learn the second and third verses, repeating the first verse at the end. Or you can provide lyric sheets or project the words on a wall or screen. Invite them to stand. Invite them to add glorious harmonies!

Unison

America, the Beautiful

Words by KATHERINE LEE BATES
Music by SAMUEL A. WARD
Arranged by NICK PAGE

Words by Katherine Lee Bates
Music by Samuel A. Ward   Arranged by Nick Page

O beautiful for spacious skies for amber waves of grain,
For purple mountain majesties above the fruited plain.
America! America! God shed His grace on thee,
And crown thy good with brotherhood from sea to shining sea.

O beautiful for pilgrim feet whose stern impassioned stress,
A thoroughfare for freedom beat across the wilderness.
America! America! God mend thine ev'ry flaw.
Confirm thy soul in self control, thy liberty in law.

O beautiful for patriot dream that sees beyond the years.
Thine alabaster cities gleam undimmed by human tears.
America! America! God shed His grace on thee,
And crown thy good with brotherhood from sea to shining sea.

Additional Verse:

O beautiful for heroes proved in liberating strife.
Who more than self their country loved and mercy more than life.
America! America! May God thy gold refine,
'Til all success be nobleness and ev'ry gain divine.

In the Hindu faith, Lord Krishna has many manifestations. One is Gopala.

FROM THE AUTHOR: One story that was shared with me told of Lord Krishna promising many women that he would dance with them on Saturday night. When Saturday came, Krishna divided into many - that "many" was called Gopala. This is a chant of praise to Gopala. The melody, like many melodies that come to North America from around the earth, has probably become westernized, changed to a major key and given a simple rhythm. This does not lessen the beauty of the chant.

Pronunciation: *Goh-pah-lah, Goh-pah-lah, Day-vah-kee-nahn dah-nah Goh-pah-lah.*

The melody should be sung in unison the first few times with the optional harmonies (in the piano RH) added later. The chant works beautifully if you take your time with it. There is a Hindu concept called Na-dha Brahma which means "the world is made of sound." Chants like Gopala help the singers attain deep meditative states where they are connected to the world through sound. It is effective to start slowly and let it speed up gradually. A simple circle or line dance would be perfectly appropriate as the song speeds up. The optional percussion adds a lot to the texture and movement of the piece.

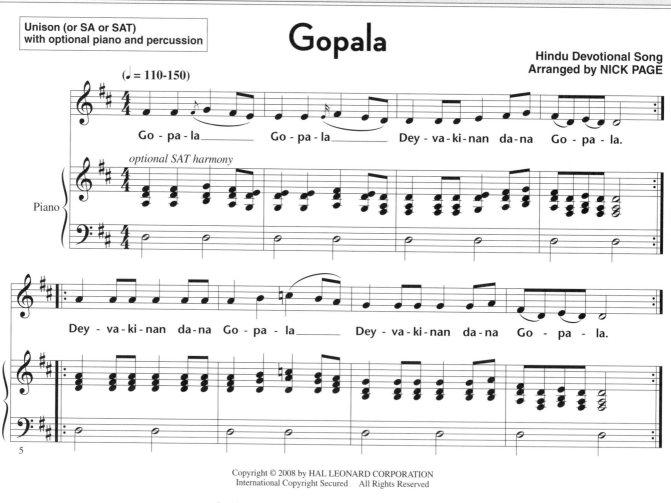

Gopala

**Hindu Devotional Song
Arranged by NICK PAGE**

Optional Percussion

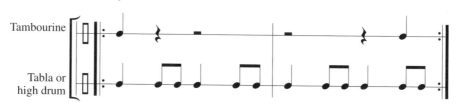

This African-American spiritual, like most spirituals, has evolved over the years. Guy and Candie Carawan learned it from Mrs. Alice Wine of John's Island, South Carolina. The songs from these islands as well as from the Georgia Sea Islands went unchanged for many generations. By the time this book's editor, Nick Page, learned it, it had become similar to the song you see here. He added some verses both original and, as is often the tradition, from other spirituals.

Spirituals constantly refer to stories from the Bible. The old Hebrew Bible has many references to "the rock" (*Tsur* in Hebrew), which is another name for God. There are many references to "honey and the rock" as well. Psalm 81, for example, reads "Open your mouth wide, and I will fill it . . . with honey out of the rock."

In recent years, accompaniments have been added, but spirituals are traditionally sung *a cappella*. This song may be sung in unison with soloists (or small ensembles) or in 2, 3, or 4-part harmonies. Singers should sing percussively, like they were hitting a drum with their voices (see Nick Page's "Marshmallow Technique" in the appendix). The background "Oo"s at ms. 17 & 21 are optional. The song works fine with just the solo part, but the choral responses at ms. 19 & 23 are needed. You can feature as many as eight soloists (or small ensembles), one for each verse. Soloists do not have to adhere to the melody that is written - they may embellish their melodies and add fills above the Refrain (but not the first time). Starting on the pitches C, Eb, or G (in any range), they can make up their own melodies. There is room for harmonies on the verses if sung with two or more singers. You are allowed to change the tempo and dynamics and add offbeat claps (on 2 & 4), but if you add new verses or make any other changes, be sure they respect African-American traditions.

Teach this song to your audience by rote. Using lots of emotion, have them shout back each phrase beginning with "There's honey in the rock!" When teaching it to your audience, have your singers sing the Refrain in unison, then have the audience sing it in unison with them. Once the audience knows the song, invite them to stand. They'll be ready to raise the roof!

There's Honey in the Rock

**African-American Spiritual
Arranged and Adapted with new
verses 2, 7, & 8 by NICK PAGE**

*The original purchaser of this book has permission to reproduce this song for use in one school only.
Any other use is strictly prohibited.*

REFRAIN

There's honey in the rock for all God's children, honey in the rock, honey in the rock.
There's honey in the rock for all God's children, feed every child of God.

1. Hypocrite, hypocrite, God despise; (Feed every child of God.)
   Tongues so clean, but he still tells lies. (Feed ...)

2. We can have justice if we care. (Feed ...)
   Right is right and fair is fair. (Feed ...)

REFRAIN

3. Heart to heart and hand to hand, (Feed ...)
   Together we'll push to the promised land. (Feed ...)

4. When I'm happy, I'll shout and sing. (Feed ...)
   And make the heavenly spirit ring. (Feed ...)

REFRAIN

5. One of these mornin's bright and fair, (Feed ...)
   Gonna take my flight in the middle of the air. (Feed ...)

6. One of these nights about twelve o'clock, (Feed ...)
   This whole world's gonna reel and rock. (Feed ...)

REFRAIN

7. If we're gonna be fair, we gotta open the door. (Feed ...)
   We gotta house the homeless and feed the poor. (Feed ...)

8. If the chains hold us down, we gotta break the lock. (Feed ...)
   Then we'll taste sweet honey in the rock. (Feed ...)

REFRAIN

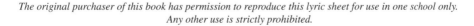

FROM AUTHOR NICK PAGE: When I was a child, my family would gather on Saturday nights to sing together. Singing with family and friends was a way of life. My two favorite songs were "Swing Low, Sweet Chariot' and "Cockles and Mussels." My grandfather would boom out the Refrain and the room would reverberate!

 Teach the song to your singers ahead of time, with the verses sung either by soloists or by unison voices. The Tutti section (measures 17 – 39) can be sung in unison or in 2, 3, or 4-part harmonies as shown (or make up new harmonies). Sing the first verse through once without piano. Stop before the Refrain and say, "This is the part we want you to sing." Then proceed into the Refrain (still in unison). Then practice the Refrain with the audience. The third verse sounds haunting if sung slowly, but go back to tempo for the Tutti section (with a rousing finish). For the children, you may have to explain what cockles and mussels are (shellfish) and that the reason Molly Malone is yelling "alive alive-o" is that in the days before TV commercials, people would advertise by yelling into people's windows, "I got fish! Get your fresh fish! Cockles! Mussels! Alive, Alive-o."

Unison or with harmony

Cockles and Mussels

Irish Folk Song
Arranged by NICK PAGE

wheeled her wheel - bar - row__ through streets broad and nar - row__ cry - ing,
each wheeled their bar - row__ through streets broad and nar - row__ cry - ing,
ghost wheeled her bar - row__ through streets broad and nar - row__ cry - ing,

F   F/A   C   C/E

All - TUTTI (harmony optional)

"Cock - les__ and Mus - sels,__ a - live, a - live - o." A-

F   F/A   C7sus   C   F

Refrain

live, a - live - o,_____ a - live, a - live - o,_____ cry - ing,

F   F/A   C   C/E

Cockles and Mussels

SINGER SONGSHEET

Irish Folk Song
Arranged by NICK PAGE

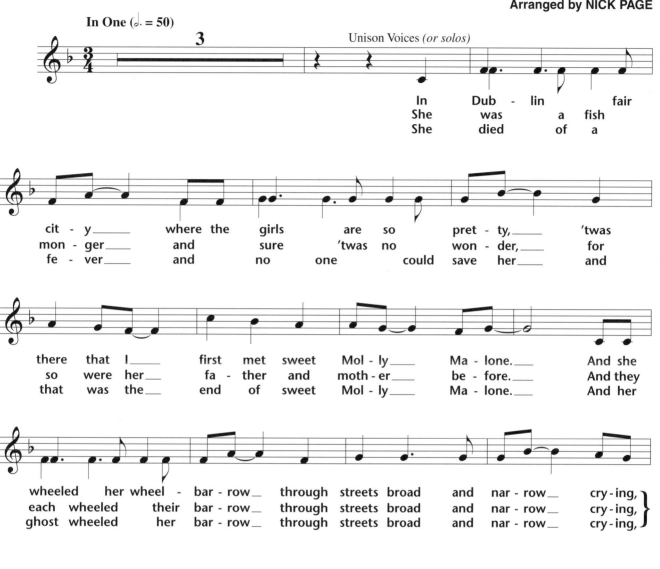

In One (♩. = 50)

Unison Voices *(or solos)*

In   Dub - lin   fair
She   was   a   fish
She   died   of   a

cit - y____   where the   girls   are   so   pret - ty,____   'twas
mon - ger____   and   sure   'twas   no   won - der,____   for
fe - ver____   and   no   one   could   save   her____   and

there   that   I____   first   met   sweet   Mol - ly____   Ma - lone.____   And she
so   were   her___   fa - ther   and   moth - er____   be - fore.____   And they
that   was   the___   end   of   sweet   Mol - ly____   Ma - lone.____   And her

wheeled   her wheel - bar - row_   through   streets   broad   and   nar - row_   cry - ing,
each   wheeled   their   bar - row_   through   streets   broad   and   nar - row_   cry - ing,
ghost   wheeled   her   bar - row_   through   streets   broad   and   nar - row_   cry - ing,

All - TUTTI (harmony optional)

"Cock - les____   and   Mus - sels,____   a - live,   a - live - o."   A-

33

The original purchaser of this book has permission to reproduce this song for use in one school only.
Any other use is strictly prohibited.

Refrain

live, a - live - o,_____ a - live, a - live - o,_____ cry - ing,

"Cock - les____ and Mus - sels,__ a - live, a - live - o."

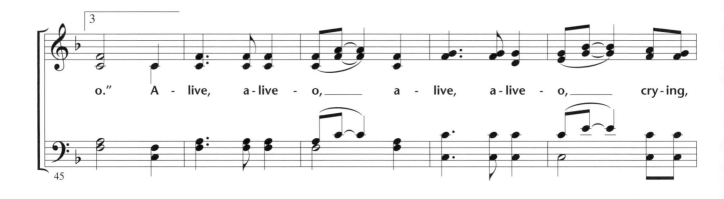

o." A - live, a - live - o,_____ a - live, a - live - o,_____ cry - ing,

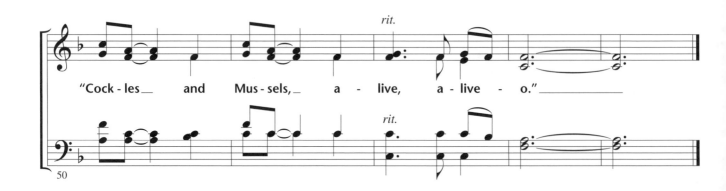

"Cock - les____ and Mus - sels,__ a - live, a - live - o."_____

The pianist and soloists may (and should) embellish. For sing-along purposes, don't worry about creating perfect unisons. Earlier styles of singing spirituals probably featured some singers improvising on the melody, creating a rich texture. They probably featured rich harmonies as well, which many people can make up if you ask them (see appendix). Clapping on the offbeats works best if you reserve it for near the end of the song (or as the spirit moves you). You can repeat the Refrain as the spirit moves you at the end! The more you get the music off the page and start creating your own voice, the more the music comes alive. As with all music, show respect to the source and make changes only as the style allows.

Unison

Swing Low, Sweet Chariot

African-American Spiritual
Arranged by NICK PAGE

REFRAIN
Swing low, sweet chariot,
    Comin' for to carry me home.
Swing low, sweet chariot,
    Comin' for to carry me home.

1. I looked over Jordan and what did I see,
    Comin' for to carry me home.
   A band of angels, comin' after me.
    Comin' for to carry me home.

REFRAIN

2. If you get there before I do,
    Comin' for to carry me home.
   Tell all my friends I'm comin' there too.
    Comin' for to carry me home.

REFRAIN

3. I'm sometimes up and sometimes down,
    Comin' for to carry me home.
   But still I know I'm heavenly bound.
    Comin' for to carry me home.

REFRAIN

If you ever bring your singers to a Senior Center (which you should), "Tell Me Why" is a song their grandparents might have sung for them when they were young and I'm sure they would love to sing along. You can also sing some other golden oldies like "Take Me Out to the Ballgame," "Give My Regards to Broadway," or some selections from musicals. Don't be afraid to sing all kinds of music including the latest grooves. They will sing along enthusiastically and everyone will have a great time. TIP: Before you sing, have your singers individually greet everyone. This will relax your singers who sometimes won't know how to behave with seniors. The seniors will set them straight: be yourself!

Tell Me Why

Tell_____ me why_____ the skies are blue?
Be - cause God made_____ the skies so blue.

And I will tell you just why I love you.
Be - cause God made you just is why I love you.

Tell Me Why

SINGER SONGSHEET

Traditional
Arranged by NICK PAGE

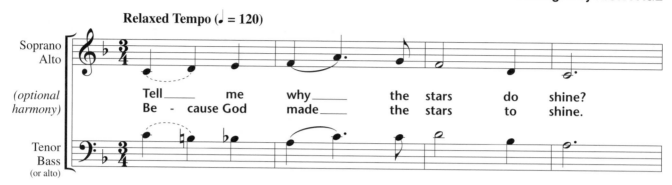

The original purchaser of this book has permission to reproduce this song for use in one school only.
Any other use is strictly prohibited.

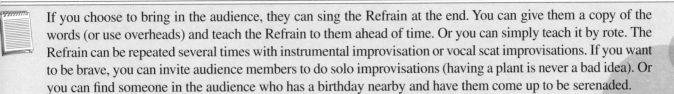

If you choose to bring in the audience, they can sing the Refrain at the end. You can give them a copy of the words (or use overheads) and teach the Refrain to them ahead of time. Or you can simply teach it by rote. The Refrain can be repeated several times with instrumental improvisation or vocal scat improvisations. If you want to be brave, you can invite audience members to do solo improvisations (having a plant is never a bad idea). Or you can find someone in the audience who has a birthday nearby and have them come up to be serenaded.

If you have a piano player who can improvise, you can have a vocal soloist sing the whole song, first in a slow lounge singer style with the pianist adding lots of corny fills and rolls. The harmony Alto/Tenor line is optional. The piece works fine whether sung in unison, two part or three part.

Have fun with this one!

> **Unison with optional
> Alto or Alto/Tenor**

Birthday Swing

By NICK PAGE

89

Birthday Swing

SINGER SONGSHEET

By NICK PAGE

FROM NICK PAGE: This anthem was inspired by the Hippocratic Oath – the oath that doctors have taken for thousands of years as a promise not to turn their science against humanity. I paraphrased such lines as "In every house where I come I will enter only for the good of my patients." "I will prescribe a regimen for the good of my patients . . . and never do harm to anyone . . . though it would profit me." When I came to the line, "To impart to my sons and the sons of the master who taught me," my wife Nita Penfold (who is a poet) suggested including the daughters.

"A Promise I Will Keep" is, of course, for all of us. Doing good does not mean performing miracles; it is the basic goodness of our daily lives. There is a reference in the piece to the Seventh Generation. This is a Seneca concept that points out that everything we do effects our great great great grandchildren.

If you choose to sing this with an audience, bring them in on the Refrain. Print the words to the Refrain in your concert program or project the words on the wall. Teach the song to your audience first, phrase by phrase. Warn them ahead of time about the gospel-style repeat at the end of the last Refrain where we sing the phrase, "This is a promise" three times.

Some Style Pointers: The tenuto symbol means something different in this style. It refers to a slight slide up to the pitch. The staccato accent symbols refer to "pings," a term that refers to percussive singing. In general, all the notes should be sung percussively, as if you were hitting a drum with your voice – even in the legato phrasings. The pings are not staccato, but are simply short accents. The conductor is at liberty to make additional stylistic changes, such as adding swells. Whatever you do, don't forget to bring joy!

The Refrain may be sung in English or Spanish.

A choral arrangement in SATB (#08745514) is available from Hal Leonard Corporation, Audio Trax (#08745515).

Commissioned by the Teaneck Community Chorus, Steve Bell, Director

A Promise I Will Keep

Words by NICK PAGE and NITA PENFOLD
Music by NICK PAGE

Unison with Audience and optional Solos

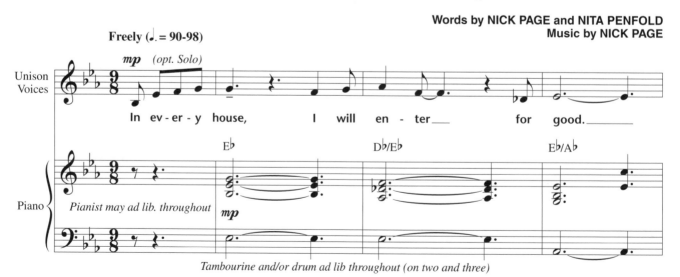

and if I am asked to turn my thoughts

toward harm, toward hate, _____ and if I am

asked to turn my life toward harm, toward hate, _____

I _____ would re - fuse. _____

(2nd time) **D.S. al Coda**

daugh-ters of the sons of daugh-ters,___ for all the prom-ise,___ hopes,___ and

dreams___ for sev - en___ gen - er - a - tions.___

Refrain

This is a prom-ise___ I___ will keep.___

(Please note: The octavo version repeats back to the beginning here.)

This is a prom-ise___ I___ will keep.___

Signal audience to repeat or have
someone sing or speak "This is a promise"
between the phrases as a cue.

INTRODUCTION
In every house, I will enter for good.
In every field, I will do only good.
By every river, I will turn my hand toward good.
This is a promise I will keep.

REFRAIN
This is a promise I will keep.
This is a promise I will keep.
I will turn my hand toward good.
This is a promise I will keep.

1. And if I am asked to turn my hand
toward harm, toward hate,
And if I am asked to turn my thoughts
toward harm, toward hate,
And if I am asked to turn my life
toward harm, toward hate,
I would refuse.

REFRAIN

2. For all of the dreams of the children,
daughters of the sons of daughters, for all their dreams.
For all of the hopes of the children,
daughters of the sons of daughters, for all their hopes.
For all of the promise of the children,
daughters of the sons of daughters,
For all the promise, hopes, and dreams
for seven generations.

REFRAIN

NOTE: This is a silly song and should be treated as such. The singers should poke fun at Pop songs in this style. Have fun with it. Add a skit or dialogue or a DJ introducing the song.

Unison with optional Audience at end

Sing a Silly and Pointless Song

By NICK PAGE

1. Sing a silly and pointless song.
   Sing it all, all day long,
   For years and years,
   'Til it comes out your ears.

REFRAIN

Sing with me Little Bo-Peep,
I'll put you right to sleep.
Sing with me on and on.
This song will make you yawn, make you yawn!

2. When we sing a silly song
   And it seems far too long,
   We laugh awhile,
   'Cause laughing makes us smile.

REFRAIN

Sing with me Little Bo-Peep,
I'll put you right to sleep.
Sing with me on and on.
This song will make you yawn, make you yawn!

Sing a silly and pointless song.

Here is the full version of "Thula Klizeo" including the advanced dance steps. For a description of the song and its full meaning, see the echo version earlier in this book (page 24).

Thula Klizeo
(the full version)

Unison or with harmony

By JOSEPH SHABALALA
Arranged by NICK PAGE

Medium Fast (♩ = 120)

Thu - la Kli - zi - o, Na - la - pa - se Ki - ya   Hey Ki___ ya, Na - la - pa - se Ki - ya.
(too lah klih zee oh nah   lah pah say ky yah)   (hay ky   yah nah   lah pah say ky yah)

When working with older singers, ask them to sing harmonies. They can make up their own (preferred) using the NICK PAGE NO FAULT HARMONY SYSTEM (see appendix) or they can use the suggested harmonies below (taught by rote).

Thu - la Kli - zi - o, Na - la - pa - se Ki - ya   Hey Ki___ ya, Na - la - pa - se Ki - ya.

The advanced version of the "Thula Klizeo" dance is optional. They can use the same dance as in the echo version. The advanced dance also has singers in lines, but it requires moving forward and backward, so it can't be done on risers.

(begin with weight on L foot)
R crosses in front of L
L passes behind R
R passes in front of L
(Do this step three times while stepping backwards; with each step getting one quarter note beat; so it's **R**LR, **L**RL, **R**LR – the underlines indicate a stomp. At the end of this, your weight should be on your R foot.)

Do three small gallups forward with the Left foot (one skip per beat). (So far, the meter has been 1 2 3, 1 2 3, 1 2 3, 1 2 3. The song is in four. Polymeters like this are common throughout African music, but you might not want to confuse your dancers quite yet with this information.)

Your weight is now on your Left foot.
Lift R knee and clap hands in front of your face.
Lift L knee and raise hands high in the air.
This last part has four beats (R knee up with clap, then down, L knee up, then down).
Your weight should now be on your Left foot. Now go back to the top without stopping.

To teach it, break it up into three parts: 1) the cross section, 2) the gallup, and 3) the R knee, L knee motion. Then teach the transition from 3 to 1. You can simplify the cross step (1) and simply have them step backwards RLR LRL RLR with a stomp on every third beat. Learn the dance before attempting to teach it. It's tricky, but worth the work.

LINE DANCE: There are two types of simple line dances. For the first one, the dancers line up behind each other and either march in formation or do the scissor step (grapevine step – walk sideways with the right foot crossing in front of the left foot and the left foot crossing behind the right foot). The leader leads the line around the space, sometimes randomly. The second type of simple line dance features everyone in a circle facing inward. Participants dance to the right or left, but stay in the circle. Hands can be held (low or high) or hands can be placed on the shoulders of the dancers on each side.

SPIRAL DANCE: Start with everyone in a large single circle holding hands. Leader takes the left hand of one of the dancers so that the person on that dancer's right will become the end of the line. The leader leads the line slowly inward (on the inside of the circle) circling close to the outside rim. Encourage the dancers to keep to the outside (and not wander into the middle). The spiral will get tighter and tighter. When the leader has reached the center, he or she makes an immediate left about-face, weaving back out of the spiral between the lines that are still spiraling toward the center. When the leader exits the circle, make another left about-face and circle around the throng of joyous dancers. With larger groups, you can begin by forming an inner and outer circle. The trick is to make these two circles into one line. The leader takes the left hand of someone in the inner circle. The person that had been on that person's right now joins their left hand with the right hand of someone in the circle behind them. The person to that person's right now becomes the end of the line.

ENTER OR EXIT SINGING: As an alternative to the choral practice of walking onstage (or off) accompanied by awkward applause, have your singers enter and exit singing a song. It can be slow or fast depending on what mood and pulse you want to create. The audience can, of course, sing along. It's very exciting.

A CAPPELLA: singing without any instrumental accompaniment.

UNISON: a melody that features one pitch at a time.

HARMONY: singing more that one pitch at the same time.

TUTTI: all the voices singing at the same time.

IMPROVISATION: to improvise or make up something on the spot. Improvisation can be a fun and accessible activity. It can be simply changing a rhythm, a word, or a style. You can improvise on a melody by changing the direction of the pitches (up or down). Making up harmony is a form of improvisation (see NO FAULT HARMONY below). For the unison songs, particularly those in the African-American style, an improvised soloist adding counterpoint between the lines adds a lot to the music.

A FUTURE COLLECTION WILL FEATURE ROUNDS, PARTNER SONGS AND SONGS TO PLAY WITH.

APPENDIX TWO: Nick Page SING WITH US Choral Series (Hal Leonard, publisher)

- "Building Bridges" arranged by Nick Page for Children's Choir, SATB Choir and Audience with piano and optional bass and percussion (#08744831)

- "The Earth's Been Good to Me" arranged by Nick Page for SAB any combination and Audience with piano (#08745653)

- "Go Where I Send Thee" sing-along arranged by Nick Page and Keith Hampton for SATB any combination, Solo and Audience with piano (#08745516), Audio Trax (#08745517)

- "A Promise I Will Keep" by Nick Page for SATB (optional Unison), Solo and Audience with piano and optional bass and percussion (#08745514), Audio Trax (#08745515)

- "Shine, Shine, Shine" spiritual arranged by Nick Page for SATB (optional Unison), Solo and Audience with piano (#08745508), Audio Trax (#08745513)

APPENDIX THREE: Four Simple Song-Leading Guidelines

Based on "Sing and Shine On" (© 2002) by Nick Page (www.worldmusicpress.com)

GUIDELINE ONE is to make every group sound fantastic. No one enjoys doing anything poorly. Mediocrity has no emotional reward. It breeds more mediocrity and that breeds discipline and other problems. Make the singers sound great. Make the singers great, period.

Here are some simple tips:

• Create a Positive Environment
In this songbook, there is a simple echo song called "The ZEST Song." The children sing, "We are the best!" This attitude is central to creating a positive environment. Expect the best, the best discipline (which means the best focus) and the best singing. The song goes on, "I'm not better than you, You're not better than me." Singers must respect each other – support each other. There are a lot of adults in the world who no longer sing because other children (or teachers) made fun of their voices when they were children. There is no room for ridicule in a supportive environment. The song continues, "We have no 'blahs'." Engage them emotionally. We're talking operatic proportions. Singing is, at its core, an emotional experience. When we open our mouths to sing, the sound that comes out is pure emotion. The more singers let out their emotions, the more engaged they would be. Engage them physically – hand signs and movement.

• Echo Technique
As outlined in the ECHO song section of this book, echo songs are simple and easy for any group to sing. It is essential, however, that we never DUMB DOWN. If the singers don't echo accurately, tell them so (with a smile) and then ask them to do a simple thing: LISTEN. Don't tolerate lazy ears (or lazy minds). Make them listen. Wake up their ears. Wake up their minds. The echo song is a perfect tool for this. But it's not enough just to echo the pitches and words. They must also echo the emotions. I call this "dynamic listening" – listening with heart, mind, and body. This leads to being engaged in heart, mind and body.

I often begin a sing with a simple echo activity. It creates confidence in the audience, particularly if I make them sound great. It wakes up their ears and prepares them for learning more challenging songs. And it engages their emotions, always the key element.

• Nick Page Marshmallows in the Mouth Technique

So how do we make a group of non-singers sound great? People new to singing often sing in a mushy and unenthusiastic manner. Say this to them, "Hold out your hands." They mimic all the motions. "Pretend that your hand is full of marshmallows." "When I give the signal, put the marshmallows in your mouth and repeat after me." They pretend to fill their mouths with marshmallows. You then sing a phrase of a song you are learning, but sing it with a marshmallow-in-mouth mushiness. They echo (or sing along with you the first time). Now you say, "Chew the marshmallows. Swallow the marshmallows. Now pretend that your voice is like a drum. You're going to hit the note as if you were hitting a drum." You then demonstrate the same phrase with them echoing. You conclude, "This is called 'Percussive Singing,'" and then add, "Do you notice how much better you sound?" To congratulate good work, I often give the hand sign from "The ZEST Song" where they pretend to polish their fingernails on their shirt lapels (as a silent signal that they're THE BEST).

• Break the Ice Technique

Sometimes people refuse to sing. At schools, this is usually the older student, particularly the older boys. It is easy to grow frustrated at this dilemma and blame ourselves for not engaging their emotions and their singing. But sometimes the simple truth is that the singers themselves are the ones who can "break the ice." The "ice" is a wall we all create to shield us from having to feel or express emotions. So the trick is to eliminate the wall and give permission for them to express their emotions through song. Within minutes of beginning a sing, I will find a charismatic member of the audience and have them come up front (sometimes more than one student). If I were teaching "The ZEST Song," I would have my "volunteer" echo the motions with me (they don't have to sing). The "volunteer" will usually put on a great show giving the gesture a real Broadway flourish. The audience will respond enthusiastically and instantly there will be a change. The "volunteer" has broken the ice, torn down the wall and given everyone permission to let out their emotions and sing. Throughout a sing, I will continue to bring up volunteers. The audience echoes the emotions of their peers. At school events, it is very exciting to "volunteer" teachers to come up to help with dance movements, play-acting, or singing.

• Smiles and Frowns Technique

To demonstrate how central the emotions are to singing, try the "Smiles and Frowns" Technique. Bring up a "volunteer." If it's a volunteer with an upcoming birthday, that's even better. Ask the volunteer to give everyone a great big happy face. Have the audience mirror the happy face. Then ask for a sad, pouty face (with audience mirror), then an angry face. Explain that everyone is going to sing "Happy Birthday" to your volunteer (make sure everyone knows the person's name). Explain that when you say "happy face," everyone is to sing with a happy face. When you say "sad face," they sing with a sad face, doing the same with an angry face. For the four phrases of "Happy Birthday," I usually do happy, sad, happy, angry. Then sing the song with these facial expressions. Everyone will be amazed at the results. The phrases with happy faces sound happy and the phrases with sad faces sound sad. Bring home to everyone how central these emotions are to singing.

Next step: Say, "Now I want you all to show happiness in your faces, but don't sound happy. Show sadness, but don't sound sad. Show anger, but don't sound angry. These are called, 'Isolation Exercises.'" Call out the emotions as everyone sings "Happy Birthday" again. They will see that it is a great challenge. You can supplement this activity by having them walk around the room showing happiness, then sadness, and then anger. Then have them isolate their movement and singing – moving with one emotion and singing with another – not an easy trick – but fun!

• Nick Page No Fault Harmony Technique

With older singers who have already learned to sing in tune, ask them to make up harmonies. You may have to explain to them first what a harmony is. Use a simple song like "There is More Love Somewhere" (page 62) or a well-known song like "Happy Birthday" or "Amazing Grace." Introduce the "Nick Page No Fault Harmony Technique." Say, "It is like No Fault Driving Insurance where you drive until you hit something, then turn. With No Fault Harmonies, you find a note that sounds good. Keep singing that note until it doesn't sound good anymore. Then find a new note. And if you sing the wrong note, it's nobody's fault." You can demonstrate this technique by having a small group of the audience sing the melody with you singing one note, switching notes when appropriate. Then have half the audience sing the melody with the other half making up a harmony. Be sure to give both sides their starting pitches. Then switch sides, with the other half making up a harmony, perhaps giving them a different starting note. This simple technique works surprisingly well. Audience members find themselves stumbling into wonderful harmonies – harmonies that could never be reproduced on the written page. Sing the song a few times allowing everyone to be creative. By the end, they will be wondrous (see Guideline Two below). Be sure to choose a simple sing. Some songs harmonize better than others – repetitive phrases are a good thing to look for.

• Own the Song Technique

Give the audience permission to "own the song." If you are singing a simple song like "There Is More Love" or "Amazing Grace," invite singers (a few would be fine) to improvise counterpoints to the melodies. These are phrases that weave between the phrases of the song (using the words of the song itself). Sometimes magic happens. You create something completely new. An old song is reborn. You "own the song." The folk process comes alive when we give ourselves permission to make these subtle changes. "There Is More Love" is a zipper song. Ask the audience for a new word like "There is more light somewhere" or "There is more justice somewhere." All changes must be made with great respect to the tradition from which the song evolved. You would not, for example, want to sing, "There is more bubblegum somewhere."

Making up harmonies, making respectful changes to the words, adding counterpoint, singing the song high, low, fast, slow, or adding a variety of instrumental accompaniment: These are all simple changes that will give everyone a sense of ownership, an empowerment where they feel that this song exists because we are singing it. And then they may come to the realization that when we change the song, the song changes us. A folksong like "This Little Light of Mine" can sound lifeless. When we invite audience members to add new words, movement, harmonies, counterpoints, and claps, the song comes to life. By owning the song, we create a greater empathy for the song and its culture. We create a firsthand experience where our voices mean something – our singing together as a community means something.

• Tips for Teaching People to Sing in Tune

Many adults stopped singing as children after someone told them that they were out of tune or that they should "mouth the words." Singing is a very emotional activity, so being told you can't sing can create a deep wound. For this reason, it is essential to have a supportive environment. No child should be allowed to criticize or make fun of another child's voice. A positive environment is one where every problem has a solution and where everyone supports each other, solving problems together.

1. Here is the simplest place to begin: Sing songs that are easy to sing in tune. With younger children this means songs with the descending minor third (na na, na na, na na na na na). It also means singing repetitive songs that don't have a large range of pitches (not too high and not too low).

2. For singers that are stuck in their lower voices, have them imitate a siren. On different vowels, swoop from their lowest pitches up to their highest, then back again. Use beautiful clean vowels like "Oo" as opposed to screeching. Speaking in a very high voice, have the singers echo back in their own high voices. Use high spoken phrases like, "Hello everyone," or "What a lovely day." Use a slightly operatic tone to make it fun and to help the singers discover the higher parts of their voices.

3. Try to sing in a range with the six notes from middle C to the A above as your center. Children are more apt to sing lower pitches out of tune simply because they don't hear lower pitches as well as higher pitches (see below).

4. Give the starting pitch. Using the first pitch, simply sing. "Here's your first pitch" or a similar phrase. If you're ever in a restaurant and you hear people singing "Happy Birthday" wildly out of tune, walk up to them and say, "Excuse me, I just read this great book that said all you have to do is give the first pitch and people will sing in tune." Give them the first pitch (middle "C" is a good note for "Happy Birthday") and see the results – in tune singing. There is a simple formula: If you can hear the pitch, you can sing the pitch.

5. Singers who sing the pitch too low can benefit from a simple "wind-up" technique where you ask them to slide their pitch up until they reach the note you are singing. You can pretend to wind them up as you do this. They will hear when they are singing the right note and stop sliding their pitch. With singers who routinely sing off pitch, simply ask them to stop and listen. Do this in a very positive way.

6. With boys whose voices are changing, particularly boys who don't do a lot of singing, singing the high notes becomes difficult and embarrassing. Most, at this stage, are not able to sing the low notes either. There is a range (called the "cambiata range") from F below middle C up to the E above middle C. It is a small range, but it is a range that is more comfortable for boys whose voices are changing. These boys will have to sing a simple harmony within the cambiata range. Anders Nyberg has edited two books of South African songs (see Resources). These songbooks (with CDs) have ideal parts for boys with changing voices.

7. Sing *a cappella*. Singing without the aid of instruments requires singers to focus on listening.

8. Right-handed people tend to have a hearing dominance in the right ear. For left-handed people, it is their left ear. In a chorus or classroom situation, seat strong singers by the dominant ear of the singers who need a little help. Don't do this in a way that embarrasses anyone.

Be rid of the popular misconception that some people can't sing in tune. **Singing in tune requires two simple steps. First, the singer must be able to hear the pitch. Secondly, they must be able to then sing that pitch.** The first step is key. This process of "inner hearing" is often overlooked. People who sing out of tune are either not hearing the pitch correctly or they are hearing one of the many high overtones we create when we sing. If we sing an "ah" vowel, we might not be aware of it, but we are creating high overtones two octaves and a third or fifth higher. The out-of-tune singer sometimes hears these high overtones, reproduces them accurately and then we tell them that they aren't singing the note we are giving them when they actually are. They are reproducing the high overtones. This is a complicated way of saying that we all hear differently. Children hear high sounds like the high overtones that many adults no longer hear. Adults hear low sounds that young children cannot hear. The "Oo" vowel is a safe vowel to have singers listen to and reproduce. The "Oo" vowel has relatively few high overtones and is the easiest one for singers to hear.

The next step is to get the singers to truly listen to the pitch you give them. The key word in teaching people to sing in tune is "listen." The same focus required to echo phrases accurately (see above) is required in listening (in our heads) to the pitches and singing them in tune. Expecting great things (like dynamic listening) creates great results. It should be noted that with a small percentage of singers, it is not about waking up lazy ears. Some people have hearing loss that they may or may not be aware of. The reason they can't sing a note in tune may be because they simply can't hear it. The ear (or one ear or the other) can have range gaps where it hears some pitches better than others.

GUIDELINE TWO: Create Confidence

Many people won't sing along if they feel frustrated in learning a song. For this reason, use every tool you can to create confidence. Use word sheets or overhead projections. Use written music. If teaching by rote, begin with the words only, then sing the whole song followed by short phrases that they then repeat. Do all this in a way that makes them feel good about themselves. Use some of the tricks mentioned above like percussive singing to make them sound better, then say "You are sounding GOOD!" But confidence is not your final goal. You want to transcend confidence to create awe. Using the tricks listed above, any group can sound wonderful. Creating *awe* simply means letting them shine and letting them become aware of their potential – of their light.

GUIDELINE THREE: Teach songs as if you were teaching them to yourself.

In order to create confidence, they must learn the songs well. Constantly ask yourself, "If I were learning this song, what would I need?" It may mean using word sheets or overheads. It may mean using hand signs with a reaching gesture for the word "reach" and other simple movements that are powerful tools for teaching by rote. Teaching the song will definitely require repetition, particularly if you teach by rote. Repeat the words. Repeat the phrases. Repeat longer phrases. Then when you sing the song again a week later, ask yourself, "If I had learned this song a week ago, would I remember it now?" But don't let the rote process become "dumbing down." They must work at remembering what you teach. With older youth, some song leaders say, I'll give you your part twice and that's all. You have to get it." They will. We all learn differently. Some of us benefit from hand signs and movement. Others need word sheets. Others simply need to listen to the melodies. All of us benefit from repetition.

GUIDELINE FOUR: Honor Cultural Traditions

Songs tell stories or are a part of great stories that need to be told. When we tell the story behind a song or behind the world of that song, we create empathy, an understanding in the heart. The song "Thula Klizeo" (pages 24 and 103) comes from a rich South African culture of singing and dancing. The words mean something. The dance means something. For the full power of the song to emerge, these stories need to be told. Otherwise it's just fun sounds. The Irish song "Cockles and Mussels" (page 76) tells the story of Molly Malone who long ago sold shellfish by walking house-to-house shouting, "Cockles! Mussels! Alive Alive-o." In the days before TV and radio (and the web), this shouting was called advertising. Tell this story. It gives the song meaning and it will give the song depth. Folk songs are like living things. When we sing them, they come alive again. When we tell their stories, we honor the traditions themselves and help to keep the traditions alive.

All cultures are different. To honor their traditions, we must be aware of these differences. For example, we can change the words to many folksongs (with respect). In fact, changing the words can actually honor the folk process, a process where the constant evolution of the music is part of the tradition. But with sacred folk songs like spirituals, keeping the original words honors the culture. Changing the words to these sacred songs, sometimes in order to accommodate a more liberal theology, can become a form of cultural misappropriation. It is always best to honor the original intent of each culture.

Strive to be authentic – singing the song as close to the original style as possible. But also be yourself. Know that when one culture sings the songs of another culture, something beautiful can emerge – music that honors both the other culture and your own. For further information on honoring culture, see the CHORAL FAMILY JOURNALS at Nick Page's website, **www.nickmusic.com**.

Page, Nick. *The Nick Page Songbook CD*. Twenty songs for sing-alongs.   www.cdfreedom.com 800-937-3397.

Page, Nick. *Sing and Shine On! An Innovative Guide to Leading Multicultural Song*. 1995. World Music Press, PO Box 2065, Danbury, CT, 06813-2565,10-2040,   www.worldmusicpress.com

Barnwell, Ysaye, and George Brandon. *Singing in the African-American Tradition, Choral and Congregational Vocal Music*. 1989. Homespun Tapes, Ltd., Woodstock, NY. (Six tapes or CDs where Ysaye Barnwell teaches the harmonies one part at a time – her way of keeping the songs within the aural tradition. With great background information. Highly recommended!)

Blood-Patterson, Peter, ed. *Rise Up Singing*. 1988. A Sing Out Publication, Bethlehem, PA, PO Box 5253, 18015.   (The best collection of folk song lyrics around. CDs available.)

Burton, Bryan. *Moving Within the Circle: Contemporary Native American Music and Dance*. 1993. World Music Press, Danbury, CT.   www.worldmusicpress.com   (Book and tape/CD. Very teacher-friendly. Highly recommended!)

Schmid, Will, ed. *Get America Singing . . . Again!* 1996, Volume 1 (ISBN 0-7935-6636-3). 2000, Volume 2 (ISBN 0-6340-1549-5). Hal Leonard Corporation. (Excellent songbooks prepared by MENC.)

Gold, Ben-Zion. *The Harvard Hillel Sabbath Songbook*. 1992. David R.Godine, Publisher, Inc., Boston, MA. (The second half features secular Jewish songs of great beauty with translations and piano accompaniments.)

Langstaff, John, ed., *A Revels Garland of Song, In Celebration of Spring, Summer & Autumn, Traditional Processionals, Carols, Rounds, Rituals & Children's Songs*. 1996. Revels, Inc., 80 Mt. Auburn Street, Watertown, MA 02472-3930, 617-972-8300.

Nyberg, Anders, ed. *Freedom Is Coming, Songs of Protest and Praise from South Africa for Mixed Choir*. 1999. Walton Music Corporation, Chapel Hill, NC. (Great book and tape of SATB songs and chants. Also Freedom Is in Your Hand, 2003.)

Orozco, Jose-Luis, ed. Ill. by Elisa Kleven, *De Colores and Other Latin-American Folk Songs for Children*. 1994. Dutton Children's Books, New York, NY. (also Diez Deditos, Ten Little Fingers)

Page, Nick, www.nickmusic.com Nick Page website with multicultural essays, catalog of publishes octavos, books, and CDs plus information on Nick's sings and workshops.

Parker, Alice. *Creative Hymn Singing*. 1976. Hinshaw Music, Inc., Chapel Hill, NC, P.O. Box 470, 27514.

Scott, John Anthony & Scott, John Wardlaw. *Ballad of America, A History of the United States Through Folk Song*, Revised 3rd Edition, Published by Folk Song in the Classroom, PO Box 23, Holland, MA 01521-0023. (Great American songs telling a great history – wonderful stories accompany each song. Highly Recommended.)

Seeger, Pete. *Where Have All the Flowers Gone, A Singer's Stories, Songs, Seeds, Robberies*. 1993. Sing Out Corporation, Bethlehem, PA.